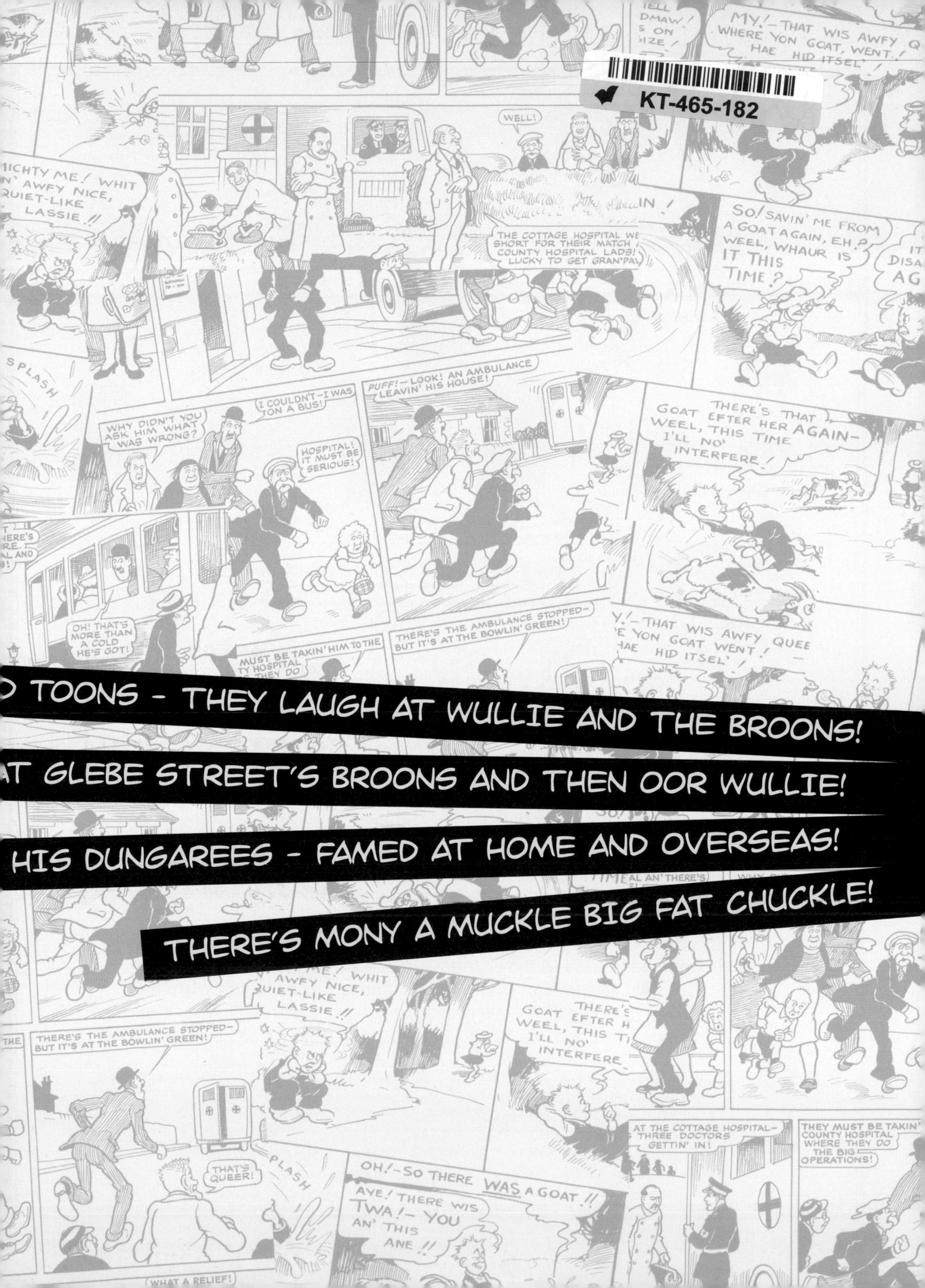

Family fun through the years – that's certainly what the Broons
and Oor Wullie have provided for their readers. In this latest collection of
classic stories, we take a look at the lives of the well-loved characters and
their friends and families as they face up to the trials and tribulations of
everyday life – both at home and further afield.

Prepare to laugh at 1937's Wullie the waiter, and share a
smile with the Broons as the younger members of the family take the law
into their own wee hands. These stories, and lots more besides, are as
entertaining today as they were when first published in The Sunday Post
many years ago. It's family fun at its best – and it's all here.

Printed and published in Great Britain by D.C. Thomson & Co., Ltd., 185 Fleet Street, London EC4A 2HS.
© D.C. Thomson & Co., Ltd., 2010.
ISBN 978 1 84535 424 4

OUT AN' ABOUT

Join the Broons as they experience their first glimpse of the But an' Ben, or when they take a trip 'doon the watter'. Then laugh with Oor Wullie as he embarks on a very special tour of Scotland and camps out with his pals.

TO THE SANDY BEACH ←

This selection of stories – taken from the days before the benefit of sun protection was known – will start you on your very own tour through the archives.

OOR WULLIE   FAMILY FUN!

The Sunday Post
28th May 1944

The Sunday Post 26th May 1940

OOR WULLIE   FAMILY FUN!

The Sunday Post
5th August 1945

The Sunday Post 10th August 1947

The Sunday Post
23rd August 1953

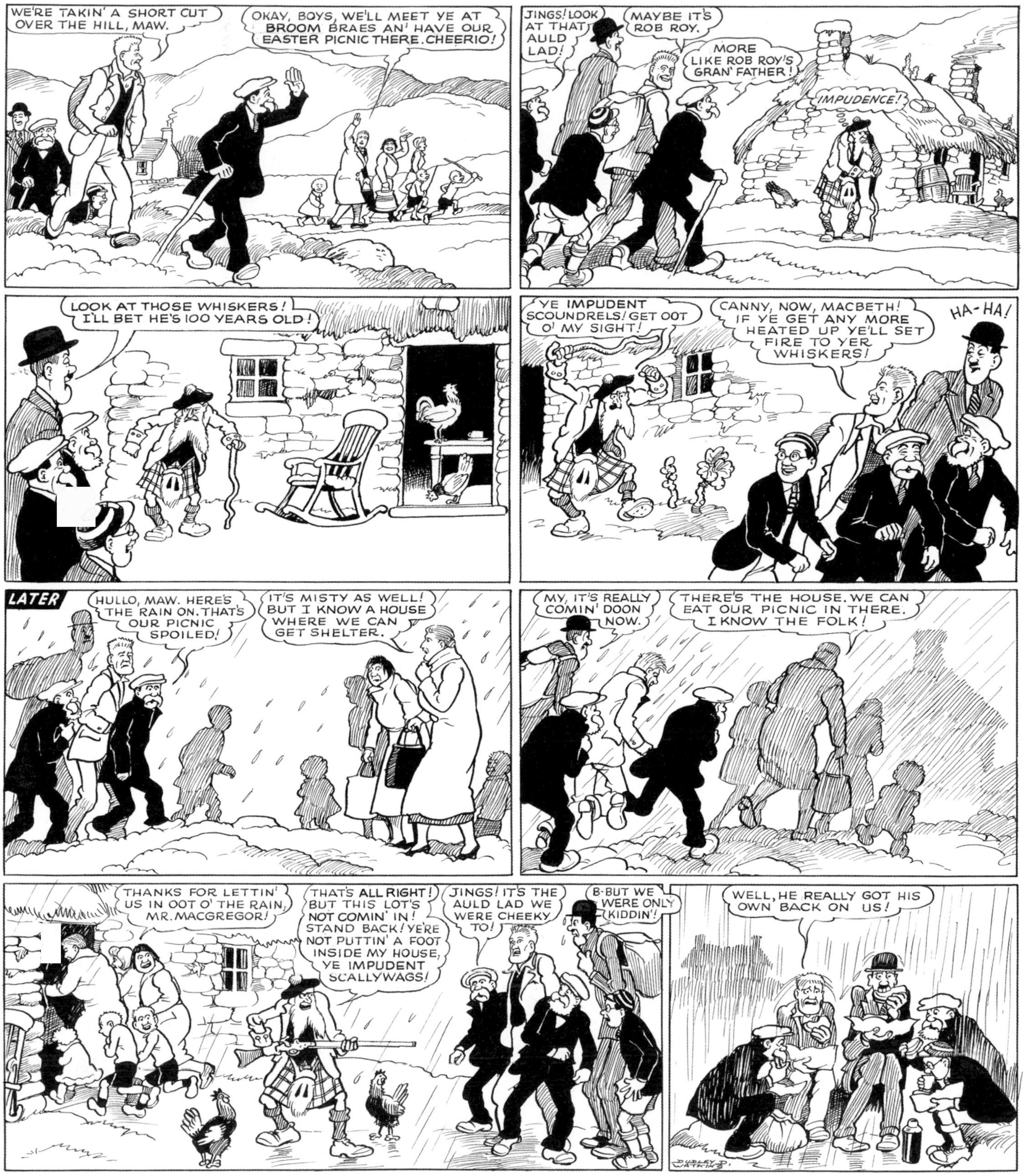

The Sunday Post 24th March 1957

1936-1939

The years between 1936 and 1939 were traumatic indeed. Not only did the country have three kings in that period, but 1939 also saw Britain and France declare war on Germany. Despite all that, the family continued to play an important part in the day to day life of most of Scotland's population.

I AM ALL FOR MILK

He's determined to grow up a big, hefty fellow like Daddy—and he evidently knows how it's done! Milk, because it contains all the food elements for strong bones, good teeth, sturdy muscles, sound nerves, is the supremely nourishing food for the whole family. Give milk — a quart a day for the children, a pint a day for the adults — improvement in health and energy almost immediately you

MILK for

ISSUED BY THE SCOTTISH MILK

Healthy living messages were designed to appeal parents. This one from the relatively Scottish Milk Marketing Board

This picture shows High Street, Perth, in the late thirties. This is still a popular family shopping area, but the 'traffic' has gone as it is now a pedestrian precinct. The shop names have changed dramatically, too.

The Annie Swan Annual

Complete Stories BY Annie S. Swan, George Blake, H.A. Vachell, Barry Perowne, Joanna Cannan, George Goodchild, etc etc.

Books such as these provided popular family reading.

The PICK of the ANNUALS

Great Gift Volumes for Young and Old

Books for the Boys—
ADVENTURE LAND, Every Boy's Annual
The ROVER BOOK for Boys
The SKIPPER BOOK for Boys
WIZARD BOOK for Boys
HOTSPUR BOOK for Boys
SPEED BOOK for Boys
FUN BOOK for Boys

For the Kiddies—
The BILLY and BUNNY BOOK
The WILLIE WADDLE BOOK
KIDDIES' PLAYTIME

and for the Grown-Ups—
AUNT KATE'S DAY-BY-DAY BOOK

Your Newsagent or Bookseller will be Delighted to Sh...

All the family was catered for here – although boys seemed to have the best deal.

DECEMBER 5, 1937.

MOST WOMEN ARE BAD HOUSEWIVES

By a Mere Man Who Knows Something About It

...d respect all women,... ...ve one serious com-...ake. Most of them... ...their houses right!... ...d plenty of chance to... ...oo. I'm a professional... ...ner, and I've cleaned... ...reds of homes.

Of course, I've seen women who were very good house-keepers. But most of them are in

germs they're a danger to health, especially in houses with children. I always clean them with alcohol. [Call it "meth." if you like.]

Many times even the most conscientious housekeeper doesn't seem to use her head.

I've actually seen women, when they were house-cleaning, clean their floors first. By the time they were through with everything else, the floor was dirty again, and had to be done over.

"Nothing worse than old shirts to clean

The article here must have caused many an angry ripple amongst the female population.

● Her whites are dazz-ling — thanks to the Rinso 2-minute boil'... And thanks to her neigh...bour for passing on... ...news about the... ...easy Rinso way to...

What every housewife needed to know.

WOMEN FREED FROM HARD WORK ON WASHDAY

(BY A WASHING CORRESPONDENT)

The Rinso 2-minute...

Rinso makes clothes brilliantly cl...

2 minutes' boiling or 12 minutes' soaking with **Rinso**

R.S. Hudson Limited

R 2445-111-55

Trams were still a popular way to travel – although many cities began a weeding out process during the 1930s.

The Sunday Post was the place to see fashions for the modern miss in 1937.

MR BOOTHBY M.P. DIVORCED

WIFE ALLEGES INFIDELITY

Lord Jamieson in the Court of Session at Edinburgh yesterday granted a decree of divorce in an undefended action at the instance of Mrs Diana Cavendish or Boothby, of St Leonards Terrace, London, against her husband, Mr Robert John Graham Boothby, Conservative M.P. for East Aberdeen, of Pall Mall, London.

The parties were married in 1935.

The grounds for the Mrs Boothby's petition infidelity.

Evidence was g and two witnesses fair Hotel, Londo Stanley Clifford tion clerk at the b Gannon, chambe about two visits Boothby and a woma last December.

"ETTRICK

Divorce was uncommon and usually made the headlines – especially if it concerned someone in public office.

Bowling! As popular today as it was back then. Note the lack of ladies, though. Perhaps they were inside making the tea!!!

'Luxury' coaches such as the one shown here were the choice of modern, 1930's day trippers.

OOR WULLIE FAMILY FUN!

The Sunday Post
17th June 1956

The Sunday Post 18th May 1958

OOR WULLIE   FAMILY FUN!

The Sunday Post
25th October 1959

The Sunday Post 5th September 1965

The Sunday Post 7th December 1941

ARE YE MAKIN' THEY SCONES FOR ME MAW?

IT'S FOR A PAIRTY TH'NICHT.

CAN I BRING MA PALS?

NA, YE'RE TAE GANG TAE BED, IT'S JUIST FOR GROWN-UPS!

IT AYE GIVES YE PLEASURE TAE GIVE PEOPLE A TREAT. REMEMBER THAT, WULLIE!

FANCY WASTIN' A' THEY SCONES AN' COOKIES ON A LOT O' AULD FIZGIGGS!

RESTAURANT

I WISH I WIS A WAITER

LUNCH 3/6

RESTAU

I'LL BE A WAITER WHEN I GROW UP, THEN I CAN EAT A' DAY!

Wullie

MIND THE HOOSE WULLIE, I'M GAEIN' A MESSAGE!

I'LL STAY IN, I'M PLAYIN' AT WAITERS!

IDEA

COME ON IN, YOU FELLERS! I'M PLAYIN' AT WAITERS!

WULLIES HOOSE

WEEL, YE TOLD ME IT WIS A PLEASURE TAE GIE FOLKS A TREAT!

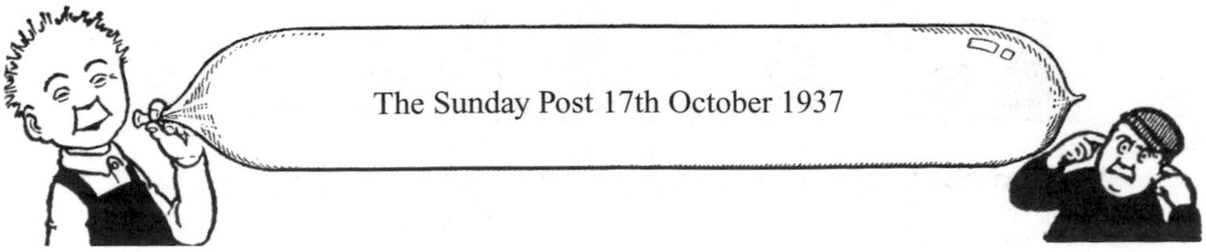

The Sunday Post 17th October 1937

The Sunday Post 27th May 1956

OOR WULLIE FAMILY FUN!

The Sunday Post 27th January 1952

The Sunday Post 15th January 1961

Panel 1: (Wullie leaning, looking glum)

Panel 2: SUP UP YOUR SOUP, WULLIE. YE'VE ONLY HAD A COUPLE O' SPOONFU'S! / I KEN, MA. BUT I DINNA WANT ONY MAIR.

Panel 3: HERE'S YOUR MINCE AN' TATTIES, THEN! YE'LL SURELY BE WANTIN' THEM. / NO' FOR ME, MA.

Panel 4: AN' NO PRUNES AN' CUSTARD EITHER? WHAT'S WRANG WI' YE, WULLIE?

Panel 5: HONEST, WULLIE. I THINK YE SHOULD GO TO YOUR BED. / OH, I'M A' RICHT, MA!

Panel 6: WANT A SOOK O' MY LOLLIPOP, WULLIE? / NO, THANKS, JESSIE!

Panel 7: COME ON, WULLIE! AULD MR LAWSON'S GIVIN' AWAY FREE LOLLIPOPS!

Panel 8: FREE LOLLIPOPS TO ALL CHILDREN AT 2 P.M. TODAY / JINGS! WULLIE'S NO' COMIN' IN!

Panel 9: I'VE JUST MADE YOUR FAVOURITE TART, WULLIE. TAK' A SLICE. / JINGS! TA, MRS DAVIDSON!

Panel 10: NA! I'D BETTER NO'!

Panel 11: HOME AGAIN / I'VE MADE YE A RICHT BIG TEA, WULLIE. SASSIDGES AN' CHIPS! / YE SHOULDNA HAVE BOTHERED, MA!

Panel 12: TWO MINUTES LATER / FEENISHED! BUT YE'VE ONLY HAD A CUP O' TEA AN' TWA CHIPS, WULLIE! / I KEN!

Panel 13: I THINK I SHOULD GET THE DOCTOR, WULLIE. / ACH! I'M FINE, MA.

Panel 14: SIX O'CLOCK! I'D BETTER HURRY!

Panel 15: HURRY UP, WULLIE! THE BANQUET'S JUST STARTIN'. A' THINGS ARRANGED JUST LIKE I PROMISED. / ACH! I DIDNA MIND DIGGIN' YOUR GARDEN, MISTER DOW.

Panel 16: THERE'S A' THE FOLK, LOOK!

Panel 17: JUST YE SIT HERE IN THE KITCHEN, WULLIE, I'LL GIVE YE YOURS ON THE QUIET. / OH, BOY!

Panel 18: SLOO / WHIT BRAW SOUP!

Panel 19: YUM — FISH AN' NAE CHIPS, JUST A BIT LEMON! / AWFY SWANKY!

Panel 20: JINGS! CHICKEN! / THIS WAS WORTH STARVIN' FOR!

Panel 21: ROAST BEEF AN' TATTIES NOW!

Panel 22: CRIVVENS! WHIT A FEED!

Panel 23: PUDDEN AN' CUSTARD! BOY, WHIT AN APPETITE I'VE GOT!

Panel 24: NOW IT'S CHEESE AN' BISCUITS. / CRUNCH!

Panel 25: ICE CREAM!

Panel 26: AN' A COFFEE T' FINISH AFF WI' — SLOOP!

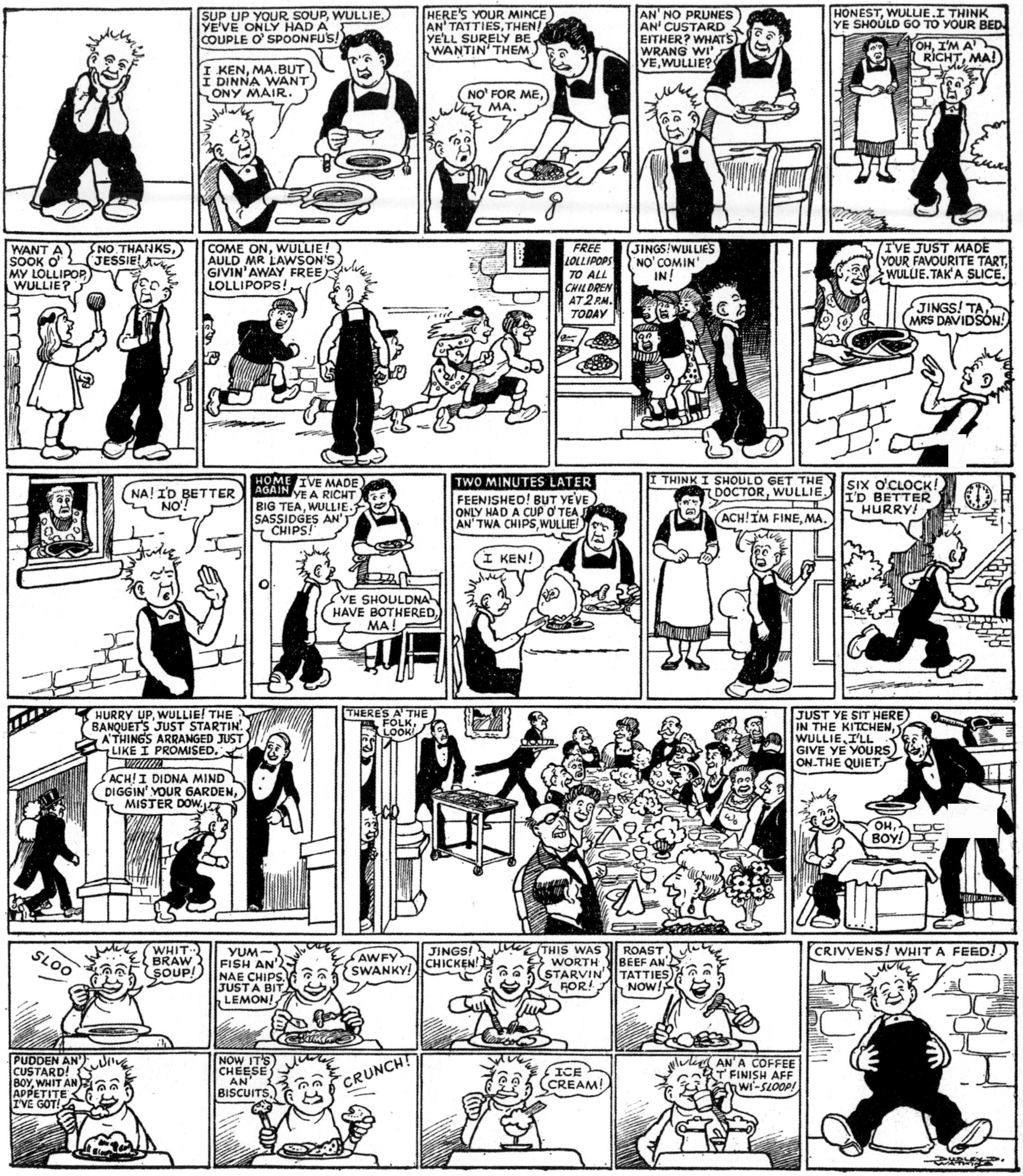

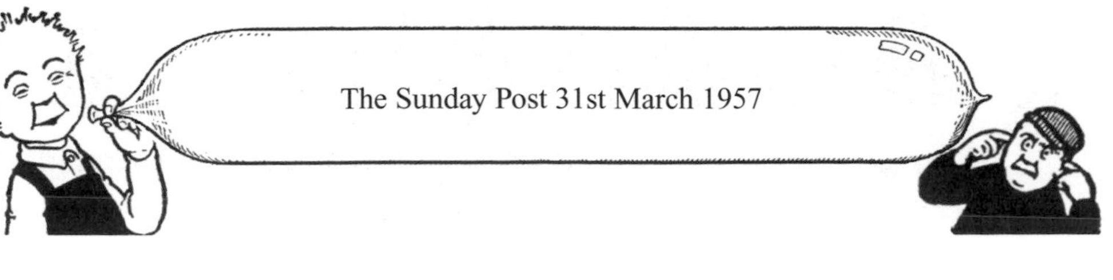

The Sunday Post 31st March 1957

The Sunday Post 1st April 1962

The Sunday Post 29th March 1959

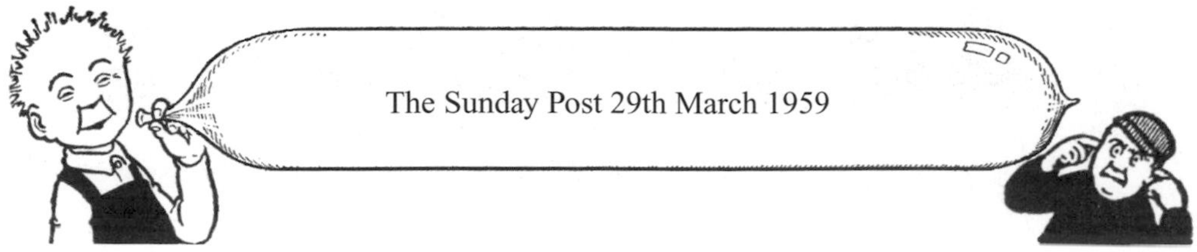

The Sunday Post 20th March 1966

1940-1944

The early forties were dominated by the war effort both at home and overseas. Families were separated as the men joined the forces and many city children were evacuated to 'safer' homes in the country. But, for people all over the country, these challenges only served to make family and community even more important.

B is for "BERMALINE"

Pat-a-cake, Pat-a-cake Baker Man.
Bake me a loaf as fast as you can.
Turn it and twist it and mark it with 'B'
For BERMALINE BREAD is the nicest for tea.

THE BAKER MAN

nourishment in ...LINE Bread
LTD · IBROX · GLASGOW
129

Is this Ad proof that eating crusts really does give you curly hair? As now, war time mums were attracted to adverts featuring babies.

The People's Friend Annual

Escapism came in the form of wholesome stories – often with a topical theme.

The Kindled Hearth
by Christine Strathern

Scouts and other group did their bit b collecting salva for the war effort.

Scenes such as this were witnessed all over the country as bombing raids hit our citics.

How do You make Broth?

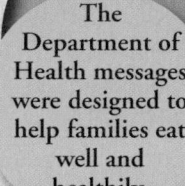

very woman has her own favourite way of making broth. But there's one thing which all women are in agreement about, and that is, that it's the vegetables in broth which help to make it such a valuable food.

Now here is a tip about making broth which is specially important today, and which you can follow, whatever method you use.

When you use cabbage or any other green-leaf vegetable—in making broth, don't put it in at the beginning with the other vegetables. Leave it until just 15 minutes before you're ready to serve—and then add it coarsely shredded, to the pot.

You see, green-leaf vegetables, especially cabbage and parsley, are extra rich in Vitamin C—the same vitamin which oranges and lemons. But this vitamin gets destroyed by long cooking. By adding the cabbage and parsley for only 15 minutes you get three times as much Vitamin C as if you put the vegetables in at the beginning.

What's more, green-leaf vegetables

taste far better this way.

If you have some of the broth left over, re-heat it next day and add more shredded cabbage, chopped parsley, sliced potatoes, and a little water 15 minutes before serving.

Why we should eat extra greens now

There is a danger to our health at present because we're not getting the Vitamin C we used to get in fresh fruit. Too little Vitamin C in our food shows itself in a feeling of tiredness and lack of energy, as well as in skin eruptions and gum trouble. These may be the early signs of more serious disease, caused by not being able to eat sufficient fruit at the present time.

But there need be no bad effects from the fruit shortage if we make up with plenty of green vegetables. They contain the same vitamin — Vitamin C — as fresh fruit does.

Green vegetables, cooked lightly, to preserve the Vitamin C, are delicious! Make a point of serving "something green" at least three times a week, if possible every day.

HOW A DUNDEE HOUSEWIFE MAKES BROTH

1 bone; 1 quart cold water; 1½ tablespoons barley; ¼ teacup dried peas; or ½ teacup split peas; 2 teacups diced carrots; 1 teacup diced turnips; 2 chopped parsley; salt and pepper.

Wash the peas and soak overnight. Wash the bone, put in a pan with the water, the barley (washed) and soaked peas and salt. Bring to the boil and remove scum. Add the chopped "root" vegetables (turnips and carrots) and simmer for 2 to 2½ hours. Add seasoning, and add the shredded cabbage 15 minutes before serving. Add chopped parsley just before serving.

Issued by the Department of Health for Scotland and the Ministry

The Department of Health messages were designed to help families eat well and healthily.

While official competitive football was suspended for the duration of the war, regional league competitions provided entertainment for those at home or troops on leave. This was the Dundee United team of 1941.

JANET MURRAY'S COOKERY BOOK

OVER 150 WARTIME RECIPES

PREFACE BY SIR JOHN ORR

Making the most of what was available. Books like this one showed women how to feed their families during the austere days of the war.

BLACK-OUT

Aberdeen	...	5.46 p.m. to 7.59 a.m.
Dumfries	......	6. 0 p.m. to 7.58 a.m.
Dundee	......	5.54 p.m. to 7.59 a.m.
Edinburgh	...	5.55 p.m. to 7.58 a.m.
Glasgow	...	5.59 p.m. to 8. 4 a.m.
Inverness	......	5.52 p.m. to 8. 9 a.m.

Moon (last quarter, 7th) rises 9.27 p.m.; sets 2.41 p.m. on Monday.

Newspapers printed information on the daily black-out time.

PASS IT ON ! ★

FOR THE NECKBAND.
WHEN shirts with collars attached shrink insert a link button into buttonholes in neckband.—Mrs Paterson, Reyston Road, Glasgow, wins this week's half-guinea prize.

PROLONG THE LIFE.
SOAK new bath towels in salt and cold water for two days. Hang out to dry. Then wash in soapy water, rinse and dry again. This strengthens bread and makes towels last longer. —Mrs M'C., Kirkintilloch.

BABY'S CHRISTMAS.
TAKE a cardboard tube from a toilet roll and put pebbles or beans into it, cover with cardboard milk top and brightly-coloured strips of wool from odd bits of wool and finish off tightly.—Miss E. Rutherford, Tweedmouth.

DRAUGHT SCREEN.
HINGE two, three, or frames together.— Dundee.

SEAL IT.
A LEAKING grid in a kitchen sink can be made watertight by filling round with hot sealing wax, if red lead is not obtainable.—A. M'Ewan, Dundee.

SARDINE TIN OPENER.
INSERT lip on tin into slit in a potato peeler. Turn gently back, removing minimum of trouble.—Mrs A.

Tips on saving money and making things last could be shared with other readers, thanks to this Sunday Post feature.

High Tig and

TIG—That's what we call it in Scotland. It is played all over the world. It is the commonest of all "chasing" games played by both boys and girls. But there are a few Scottish variations.

HIGH TIG—If you jump up on a fence or box, off the ground, they can't tig you.

LAME TIG—If you are tigged on the body or head or arm, you have to hold the part touched, when you chase the others. It's a hard job if you are tigged on the leg and have to hold it and hop !

For children, there was always time to play.

Points Rationing May Go Before Christmas

PLANNING TO INCREASE MEAT ALLOWANCE

The Christmas gift to the nation, which the Minister of Food has hinted at, may be a substantial increase in the

In October 1944 there was good news on the horizon.

Visits from a member of the Royal Family helped raise spirits during the war. Queen Elizabeth was always a favourite.

The Sunday Post 20th March 1960

The Sunday Post 13th October 1968

OOR WULLIE FAMILY FUN!

The Sunday Post 28th November 1965

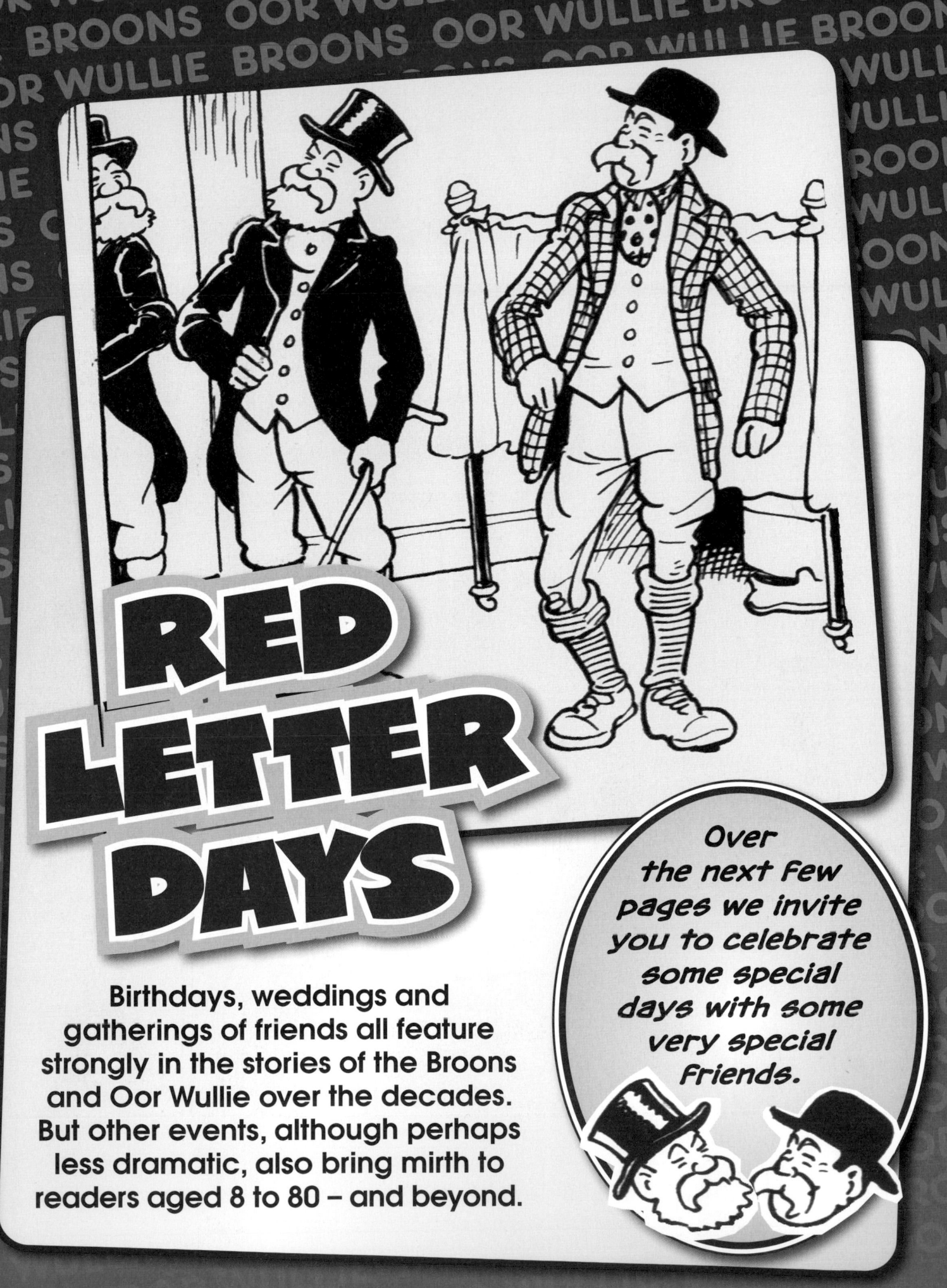

RED LETTER DAYS

Birthdays, weddings and gatherings of friends all feature strongly in the stories of the Broons and Oor Wullie over the decades. But other events, although perhaps less dramatic, also bring mirth to readers aged 8 to 80 – and beyond.

Over the next few pages we invite you to celebrate some special days with some very special friends.

The Sunday Post 1st September 1946

The Sunday Post 28th February 1937

OOR WULLIE   FAMILY FUN!

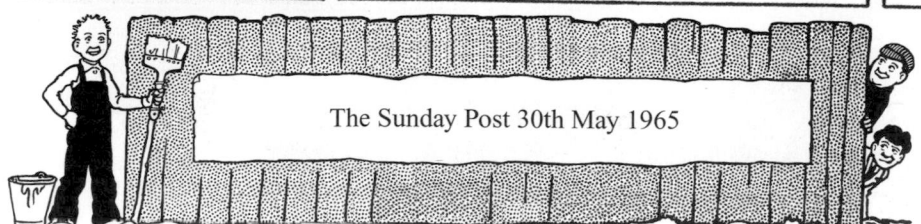

The Sunday Post 30th May 1965

The Sunday Post 5th November 1944

OOR WULLIE   FAMILY FUN!

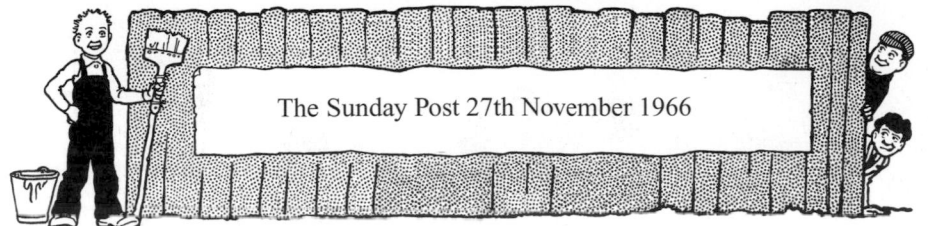

The Sunday Post 27th November 1966

The Sunday Post 10th April 1949

OOR WULLIE FAMILY FUN!

The Sunday Post 29th October 1967

The Sunday Post 15th May 1960

OOR WULLIE — FAMILY FUN!

IT'S FIXED THEN — WE'LL ROLL OUR EASTER EGGS DOON CAIRNIE BRAE TOMORROW!

AYE! WE'LL MAK' A RACE O'IT. THE WINNER GETS FIVE MARBLES FROM EACH O' THE LOSERS!

GREAT!

CHEERIO, THEN! MIND AN' BRING YER MARBLES FOR ME — HO-HO!

CHEEK!

HELLO, WULLIE!

HELLO, MA — DID YE MIND TAE HARD BOIL AN EGG FOR ME?

OH, WULLIE — I FORGOT! AND I'VE JUST USED THE LAST O' MY EGGS FOR BAKING!

OH, NO!

YE'LL JUST HAE TAE ROLL YER CHOCOLATE EGG!

ACH! IT'S NO' THE SAME!

LATER —

WHAUR'S YER EGG FOR ROLLING?

MY MA DIDNA HAE ONY. I'LL HAE TAE ROLL MY CHOCOLATE EGG INSTEAD!

HO! HO! THAT'S YOU OUT O' THE RACE. ONE BUMP AN' YER EGG WILL CRACK!

YOU'RE RIGHT! I'D BE AS WELL EATIN' IT NOW!

AYE! BUT DINNA THINK YE'LL GET OOT O' PAYIN' YER MARBLES TAE THE WINNER.

MUNCH

YE CANNA BACK OOT NOW.

TOO BAD THERE'S JUST THE TWO O' US, EH, SOAPY?

NEVER MIND, WULLIE — YE CAN TRY AGAIN NEXT YEAR!

WELL, THAT'S MY EGG EATEN. I'LL START THE RACE THEN. READY - STEADY —

FIRST PAST THE STANDING STONE WINS!

GO!

HOI!

WHIT'S WULLIE DAEIN'?

AT THE BOTTOM.

THE WINNER!

WINNER? WHIT ARE YE BLETHERIN' ABOOT?

YE DIDNA ROLL YER EGG DOON THE HILL!

WHO DIDNA? ME AN' MY EGG ROLLED DOON TOGETHER — AN' NAEBODY SAID YE COULDNA DAE THAT!

ONYBODY FOR A GAME O' MARBLES?

JINGLE

The Sunday Post 6th April 1969

The Sunday Post 14th August 1960

HELP! POLIS!

All Oor Wullie fans know and love the Auchenshoogle local bobby, P.C. Murdoch, who is much in evidence over the next few pages. Also take time to laugh at the strangest ever car number collection and discover which Broon is only too happy to end up in the arms of the law.

This next collection of stories takes a light-hearted look at all things legal – so prepare to be sentenced to a stretch of hard hitting humour.

PAW BROON   MAW BROON   HEN BROON   MAGGIE BROON   JOE BROON   DAPHNE BROON   HORACE BROON   THE BROON TWINS   THE BROON BAIRN   GRAN'PAW BROON

The Sunday Post 14th April 1940

The Sunday Post 23rd September 1956

PAW BROON · MAW BROON · HEN BROON · MAGGIE BROON · JOE BROON · DAPHNE BROON · HORACE BROON · THE BROON TWINS · THE BROON BAIRN · GRAN'PAW BROON

The Sunday Post 13th August 1950

1945-1949

The end of the war in 1945 brought great changes. While celebrations were the order of the day, there was still rationing and shortages. But the overall feeling was positive and the country delighted in the marriage of Princess Elizabeth to the Duke of Edinburgh in 1947, and welcomed teams from all over the world to London for the 1948 Summer Olympics.

The Beano, first published in the late thirties, was a firm family favourite by the mid forties. And it wasn't just the children who looked forward to their weekly dose of escapism.

The declaration of peace had people dancing in the streets all over Britain.

One of the major events of the time was the introduction of the National Health Service. This advertisement from the Department of Health for Scotland attempts to explain everything.

A cold winter brought fun in the snow for the youngsters in the family.

Mobile shops, like those shown here, were an essential lifeline for many country people.

STRATHEARN DAIRY JAMES SQUARE CRIEFF

YJ9886

YJ 9869

Give her a Hoover
—the gift she really wants

She deserves the best, doesn't she? So give her a Hoover Cleaner, the gift she really wants — the gift that goes on being remembered week after week, month after month, year after year — giving her freedom from hard back-aching drudgery.

But be sure you insist on a Hoover! That's the cleaner she wants because she knows it is the best. There is a model for every size and type of home. Prices from £10 . 10 . 0 to £21 (plus purchase tax). To ensure early delivery see your Authorised Hoover Dealer *now*.

The **HOOVER**
Registered Trade Mark

It BEATS ... as it sweeps ... as it cleans
HOOVER LIMITED PERIVALE

A Christmas present that might not be appreciated today.

Glasgow Cross in 1948 was a little quieter than it is now.

TO-DAY'S RADIO

Scottish Home Service

Light Programme

Third Programme

THE MINISTRY OF FOOD, LONDON, S.W.1. FOOD FACTS No. 442

The radio was number one for home entertainment.

Interest in the Royal Family was strong – especially when the arrival of a new baby was imminent.

900 Down With Measles Every Week

INFECTIOUS diseases are prevalent in Scottish towns. Measles heads the list in Glasgow. New cases are being reported at the rate of 900 a week.

Over 100 mumps cases are occurring in Dundee every week. The outbreak has lasted almost four months.

Chickenpox and scarlet fever are also prevalent.

Whooping cough and mumps are the chief trouble-makers in Aberdeen.

Feature of the mumps in Aberdeen and Dundee is the high proportion of grown-ups who are taking it.

Edinburgh has kept clear of any sizeable diseases

"THE DAILY HELP."
Your SALVAGE is "the daily help" to the paper-maker and the printer. so carry on THE GOOD WORK!

Trained Men...
HAVE ALL THE ANSWERS

"The direction in which training starts a man will determine his future life."—Plato.

The sound practical knowledge that countless I.C.S. students have acquired through a convenient course of Home Study has paved the way for many a successful career.

I.C.S. trained men know the answers in their trade or profession, and their applications for the better-paid posts in business and industry get the answers, too . . . from prospective employers.

Fill in the coupon, post it, and get free advice on how to join the well-paid ranks of the I.C.S. men !

INTERNATIONAL CORRESPONDENCE SCHOOLS

IF THE PRINCESS HAS A SON

WHAT name will he be given? The choice doesn't lie with the father and mother alone. The King and Privy Council must be consulted.

Choice will be restricted to Christian names used by the Royal Family. It could be George, Edward, Henry, William, Richard, John, Charles, &c

For sentimental reasons, the Princess might favour Philip. But sentiment must take a back seat.

There's nothing to prevent Philip being included in the six or seven secondary Christian names which the young prince would be given. And in private he might be called Philip.

For the first Christian name, choice might well lie between Edward and George.

Edward might finally be preferred, because this would mean a change from George, as Edward VIII. was never crowned.

The war may have been over, but there were still shortages.

Correspondence courses were seen as the answer for many men when they left the services.

Infectious diseases like measles, mumps, chickenpox and scarlet fever weren't much fun for anyone – especially the high proportion of adults who succumbed.

The Sunday Post 9th August 1959

OOR WULLIE FAMILY FUN!

The Sunday Post 14th May 1961

The Sunday Post 17th February 1963

My cartie's braw, eh? Just like a real car! Horn an' a'thing!

Jings! I dinna have number plates though!

I ken—I'll see Mister Miller! SCRAP YARD

Can I have a couple o' number plates, please? Help yersel' Wullie.

I'm a' the road now! A number all of my own! EGS 819

How's that, lads? Number plates! Bet you wish you'd some, eh? Jings! EGS 819

Oot o' the way, Eck! A real car's comin'! Ha-ha! Hey! Watch it! HONK! EGS 819

Turnin' left now! I'll stick oot my hand like other car-drivers do!

PUSH! Hey! EGS 819

Who wis that? Stop! Help! I've hit P.C. Murdoch! Good job his helmet's fallen over his eyes! He hasn't seen me yet!

Fly monkey! He's ducked down! I can't see who it is but—

Ha-ha! That wis quick thinkin'! He couldna see it wis me!

FOUR HOURS LATER. I'd a right laugh, lads! I bumped into P.C. Murdoch an' he didna ken it wis me! I wis too fly! Awa'!

Here he is now, Wullie! We'll see if ye were right!

Hiya, P.C. Murdoch! Whit are ye wantin'? I havena broken any windies for weeks! Aye, that's right, Wullie, but—

—Whit wis the idea o' knockin' me over this mornin', eh? But! Jings! Help! H-how did ye ken? Ye didna see me!

No, Wullie, but— I got yer number! Ha-ha! Oh, no! Knocked over by cartie No. EGS 819. EGS 819

My cartie wis ower much like a car!

DUDLEY D. WATKINS

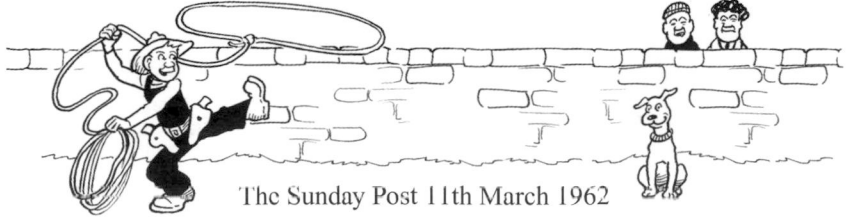

The Sunday Post 11th March 1962

PAW BROON · MAW BROON · HEN BROON · MAGGIE BROON · JOE BROON · DAPHNE BROON · HORACE BROON · THE BROON TWINS · THE BROON BAIRN · GRAN'PAW BROON

The Sunday Post 15th September 1968

TUNES O' GLORY

Scots the world over love to hear the skirl o' the pipes – albeit from a distance, preferably. And there's sure to be a note or two of discord when Wullie and the Broons turn tuneful.

The Following fun-filled pages feature everything from marching bands to one man bands, so just sit back and enjoy this Broons and Wullie style musical interlude.

The Sunday Post 10th August 1941

The Sunday Post
23rd September 1945

THE BROONS   FAMILY FUN!

The Sunday Post 26th September 1948

The Sunday Post
25th November 1951

The Sunday Post 14th February 1954

OOR WULLIE   FAMILY FUN!

HOORAY! IT'S SATURDAY MORNING. NO SCHOOL THE DAY. JUST FUN A' THE TIME.

HULLO, WILLIAM! DON'T YOU HAVE ANYTHING TO DO? SOME BOYS TAKE MUSIC LESSONS ON SATURDAY MORNING.

ACH! I COULDNA BE BOTHERED WI' THAT!

YOU WOULD LOOK WELL PLAYING A VIOLIN.

MISS KEYS PIANO TEACHER

MISS BOW VIOLIN TEACHER

HELLO, BOB! ARE YE FOR A GAME O' BOOLS?

NO! I'M GOING TO MISS KEYS FOR MY PIANO LESSON.

DOWN THE ROAD — HELLO, SOAPY! C'MON TO THE PRANNY POND.

NO! I'M GOING TO MISS BOW FOR MY VIOLIN LESSON.

HUH! BOB AN' SOAPY AN' THEIR TWA MUSIC TEACHERS ARE JUST SWANKERS.

W'S SHED

HERE'S MY MOOTH ORGAN.

WHAT'S WRANG WI' THAT FOR MUSIC?

I CAN PLAY THE CRACKERS, TOO.

THEY SOUND AS GOOD AS ONY PIANY TAE ME.

AN' JUST LISTEN TAE MY DRUM! ACH, THE FIDDLE DOESNA HAE A LOOK-IN! RAT-TAT-TAT

AN' JUST LISTEN TAE THIS! BLAST

STOP THAT ROW, WULLIE. I CANNA HEAR MASEL' CHAPPIN' THE STICKS UP.

YE'RE DISTURBIN' THE PEACE.

THAE FOWER MUSICAL INSTRUMENTS GI'E ME AN IDEA.

FIRST, I'LL FIT THE BUGLE INTAE THESE BELLOWS.

MAYBE I CANNA PLAY THE PIANY OR THE FIDDLE—BUT I'LL SHOW THEM! RING

HEY, WULLIE~ WID YE TEACH US TAE PLAY A ONE-MAN BAND?

ALL RIGHT— JUST COME WI' ME.

JUST SIT DOON, LADS. I'M BUSY WRITIN' ON THIS BOARD.

TERRIBLE!

AWFUL! SCRAPE

MISS KEYS PIANO TEACHER

MISS BOW VIOLIN TEACHER

OOR WULLIE ONE-MAN BAND TEACHER. LESSONS— 1ᴰ AN HOUR

MY! THAT'S GREAT!

THOUGHT~ THIS'LL SHOW THAE TEACHERS THAT I'M REALLY MUSICAL!

KNICK-KNACK

DONG DONG

TUT-TUT! WHAT A ROW!

WHAT A DIN!

HA-HA-HA!

HUH! NOW THEY KEN THEY'RE NO' THE ONLY ANES THAT CAN TEACH MUSIC.

RAT-TAT-TAT.

TOOT TOOT

MISS KEYS PIANO TEACHER

MISS BOW VIOLIN TEACHER

DUDLEY D. WATKINS

The Sunday Post
6th December 1953

The Sunday Post 25th May 1958

1950-1954

The country was shattered by the death of King George VI in February 1952 but, after the initial shock, the presence of the new Queen Elizabeth II helped raise spirits. In entertainment, this period saw publication of Casino Royale, Ian Fleming's first 'James Bond' book, the first appearance of Andy Pandy on television and the first West End performance of the Agatha Christie play The Mousetrap.

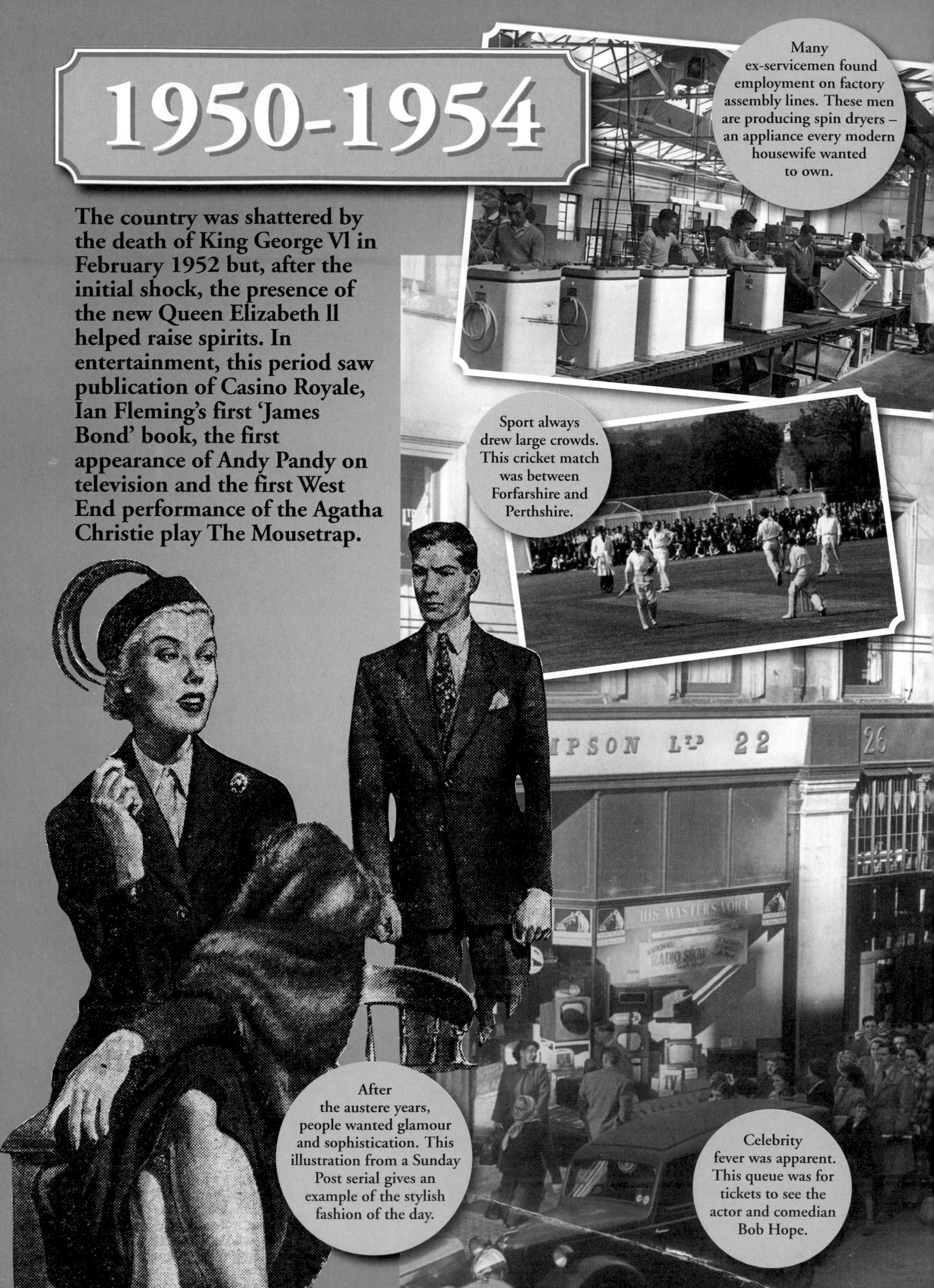

Many ex-servicemen found employment on factory assembly lines. These men are producing spin dryers – an appliance every modern housewife wanted to own.

Sport always drew large crowds. This cricket match was between Forfarshire and Perthshire.

After the austere years, people wanted glamour and sophistication. This illustration from a Sunday Post serial gives an example of the stylish fashion of the day.

Celebrity fever was apparent. This queue was for tickets to see the actor and comedian Bob Hope.

The Sunday Post
24th March 1963

The Sunday Post 7th September 1958

The Sunday Post
6th October 1963

The Sunday Post 19th February 1967

The Sunday Post
30th March 1969

When it comes to sport, the Broons and Oor Wullie might not be Olympic class – but they would certainly win gold medals for humour.

WINNERS AN' LOSERS

Laugh with Wullie as he tries his hand at wrestling and discovers the dangers of curling. And enjoy a marathon of mirth when the Broons take part in a cross country race. Ready, steady, go – for lots more fun.

OOR WULLIE   FAMILY FUN!

The Sunday Post 4th June 1939

The Sunday Post 16th May 1937

OOR WULLIE   FAMILY FUN!

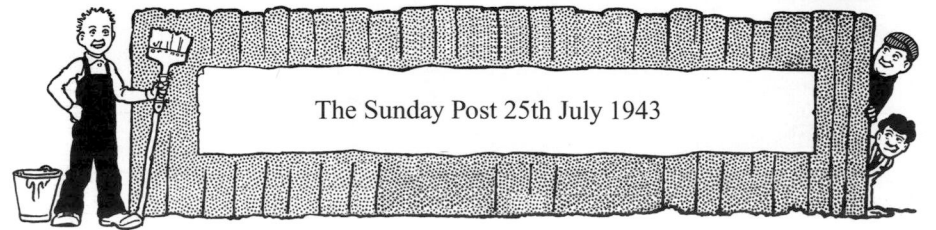

The Sunday Post 25th July 1943

The Sunday Post 22nd January 1939

OOR WULLIE   FAMILY FUN!

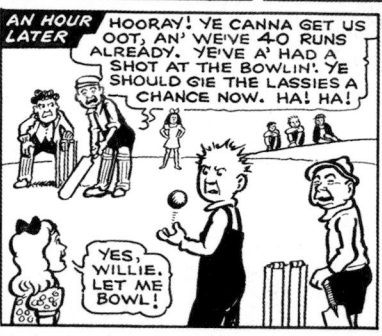

The Sunday Post 6th June 1948

THE BROONS   FAMILY FUN!

The Sunday Post 24th October 1948

OOR WULLIE FAMILY FUN!

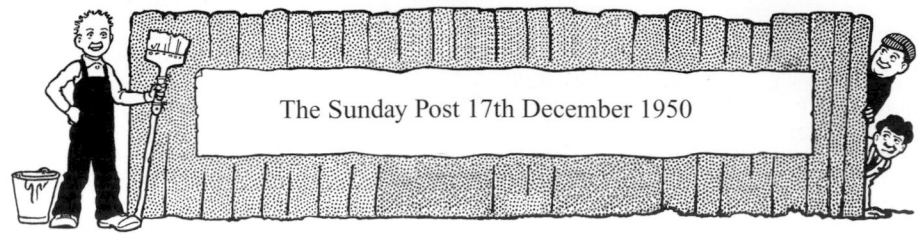

The Sunday Post 17th December 1950

The Sunday Post 10th July 1955

1955-1959

The mid fifties brought political upheaval, with Prime Ministers Churchill and Eden both resigning due to ill health, before being succeeded by Harold Macmillan. Agatha Christie was still amongst the best selling authors and, for the younger members of the family, a new TV programme called Blue Peter was broadcast in 1958. This period also saw the first televised royal Christmas message.

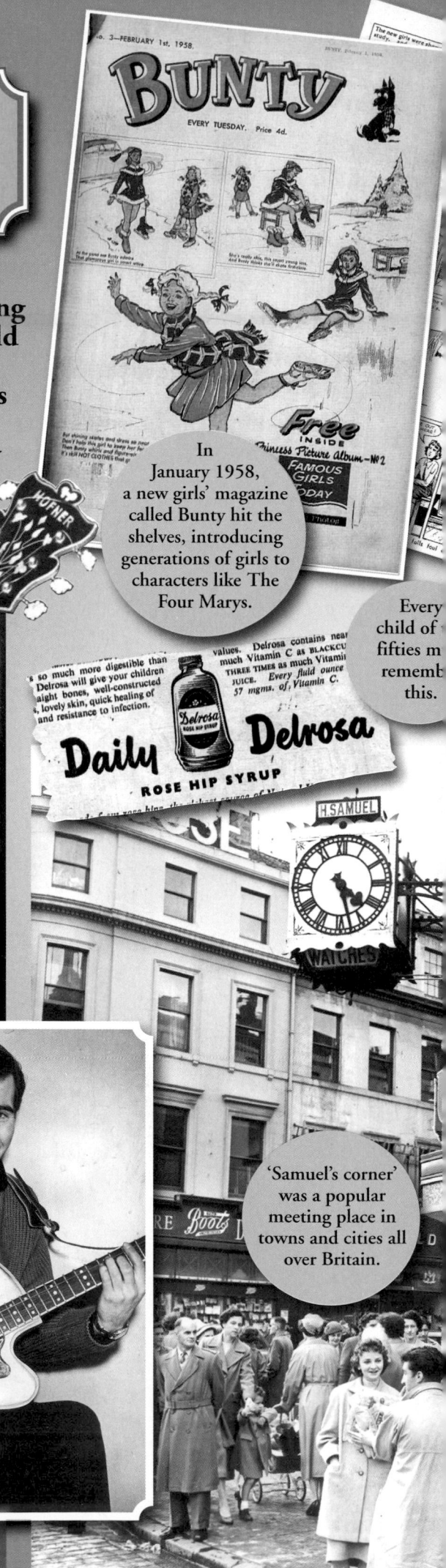

In January 1958, a new girls' magazine called Bunty hit the shelves, introducing generations of girls to characters like The Four Marys.

Every child of fifties m remembe this.

Daily Delrosa
ROSE HIP SYRUP

Two of Britain's top music stars – Tommy Steele and Jim Dale.

'Samuel's corner' was a popular meeting place in towns and cities all over Britain.

Is Hire Purchase Really A Good Thing?

LAST week a worried mother (Mrs A. J.) asked readers whether she should start buying goods on hire purchase.

All her life she has saved up for what she buys—but now her family are envious of neighbours who have TVs, radiograms, &c., on H.P. Well, the letters have fairly poured

What's the verdict?

A third of the readers advised Mrs A. J. to buy her goods on H.P. The other two-thirds are definitely against H.P. in any form. They advise Mrs A. J. to go on paying her way

H.P. was seen as the easy way to buy – but not by everyone.

TV KILLS NEW TOWN'S HOPE OF A CINEMA

...collect his...
...office in Falkirk. The suitcase...

BECAUSE over 50 per cent. of householders in the new town of East Kilbride own TV or radio sets there is no likelihood of a cinema being built in the town.

...told to Sir Patrick... the East Kilbride... ...tion, by a cinema... ...was in Scotland... that it would... owners who... with such strong...

population of... scheduled to...

The rise in popularity of TV wasn't good news for those who still enjoyed a trip to the cinema.

The young queen was the ultimate style icon of the day – even in the rain.

CANADA WANTS—
- DOMESTICS
- NURSES
- SHORTHAND TYPISTS
- DRAUGHTSMEN

For information on the ASSISTED PASSAGE Scheme apply

TRAVEL TRIPS LTD.

...D ST.,...
...hone...

RHODESIA WANTS—
BRICKLAYERS
CARPENTERS
PLASTERERS
PLUMBERS
HAIRDRESSERS
TEACHERS
NURSES
TYPISTS

Full information and Application Forms from

TRAVEL TRIPS LTD.
22 RENFIELD ST., GLASGOW, C.2.
Telephone: City 7871.

...lad To Come Home

...AM glad someone has at last given some facts regarding conditions in Canada (Mr Savage's letter last week).

For every person who is rushing to emigrate to Canada, there are at least two over there now who would change places with them and return to the Old Country.

100 dollars in Canada may be worth £37, but only at the rate of exchange —not in purchasing power. To maintain a decent standard of living there, one must have a wage of 75 dollars (over £27) at least.

Some people like Canada, I have no doubt. But anyone who has a decent job and a good home here should think carefully before he gives it all up...

Emigration was still an attractive prospect – as these cuttings show. But not every new beginning in a new country was successful.

Although many aspects of family life were changing by the day, the washhouse, or steamie, was still going strong in many communities.

Shopping in Edinburgh – this was a busy area before the St James Centre was even thought about.

OOR WULLIE   FAMILY FUN!

The Sunday Post 16th January 1955

THE BROONS   FAMILY FUN!

The Sunday Post 8th September 1963

OOR WULLIE   FAMILY FUN!

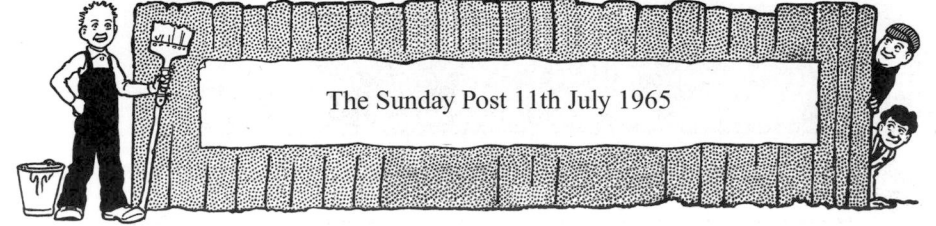

The Sunday Post 11th July 1965

The Sunday Post 4th August 1968

ANIMAL ANTICS

Creatures of every shape and size have brought extra humour to the pages of the Broons and Oor Wullie over the years – as this fun-filled choice of stories illustrates.

There's 'cat'astrophe when the Broons try to get rid of an unwelcome pet and dog-sit for a pal. And Wullie finds it's 'neigh' laugh being followed home by a horse.

The Sunday Post 29th October 1950

OOR WULLIE   FAMILY FUN!

The Sunday Post 26th November 1950

The Sunday Post 19th June 1955

The Sunday Post 21st June 1953

The Sunday Post 8th August 1965

1960-1964

The early sixties heralded a new, exciting time - although for many families the changes were slow and steady. Royal brides included Princess Margaret and Princess Alexandra and royal babies were much in evidence. TV went from strength to strength and the new satire show That Was The Week That Was pushed the boundaries further than before. On the international front, Britain and France agreed terms to build a Channel Tunnel - which was expected to take five years!

Modern factory canteens meant subsidised meals were available for workers.

This Week's TOP SHOWS

THE LUCY SHOW — The last of Lucy — and the best. Ball has a ball at the ball game! (BBC tomorrow.)

PIT YOUR WITS — Basically the same formula as before—but teams no longer compete in the IQ test. This, I'm told, is for your benefit. You can now concentrate on the questions without interruption. (BBC tomorrow.)

THE CITY—Only 500 people actually live in the City of London, yet 400,000 work there. ITV focus their documentary on this fantastic square mile. (Wednesday.)

THE BEVERLY HILLBILLIES—Move a hillbilly family from their mountain home to a mansion in California and what do you get? Laughs by the score in this new series. (Tuesday.)

Popular TV shows of 1963.

IT'S THE LATEST HAIR-DO

Young women saw shorter hairstyles as modern and liberating.

An important piece of furniture for every modern home in the sixties.

Coffee bars became popular with young people who wanted to 'hang out' with their friends.

Tape recording is the new family hobby!

Get a tape recorder and, suddenly, the whole family is using it: to learn languages or play an instrument; to record favourite pieces of music; to rehearse for the school play; to keep a sound diary of the family's life; and lots, lots more. Tape recording is the creative hobby for the whole family. For the family man, two Philips tape recorders are particularly interesting. Model EL3541/H is a de-luxe instrument with many technical features. It gives 4-track recording at 3¾ i.p.s., is very easy to operate, and has a handsome leathercloth-covered wooden cabinet for fine sound quality. Model EL3541 offers the same features in a polystyrene cabinet at a slightly lower price. Ask about Philips Family Tape Recorders at your Philips dealer.

FAMILY DE-LUXE TAPE RECORDER **42 gns.** complete
MODEL EL 3541/H

MODEL EL 3541: **36 gns.** complete

Remember—for the best results, always use Philips Tape.

POST TODAY

Philips Electrical Ltd., (Dept. 6SP6), House, Shaftesbury Avenue, London, W

Please send me more information the products I have ticked below.

☐ Philishave ☐ Twin
☐ Top Twins ☐ Tape

Name
Address

A new hobby for a new age. Reel to reel tape recorders gave many families hours of fun as people could listen to their own voices - often for the first time.

Days at the berries were great for children. Fresh air and earning money - what more could anyone ask for?

Twist competitions or marathons tested stamina and style, as young people embraced the new dance craze.

'Terylene' puts the prettiest skirts on quick-witted girls

Man-made fibres were hard wearing, smart and easy to launder in the new washing machines.

The instantly recognisable Trojan Bubblecar was a symbol of the time.

JIMMY LOGAN SAYS:
"YE CANNA BEAT THIS if ye face PLAIN FACTS!"

The plain facts are that of all the leading washing machines on the market Duomatic is the only one that gives you

Celebrity endorsement was seen as a winner - even in the sixties.

LOXENE HAIR CREAM EASY-TO-ENTER COMPETITION

6 MINI-MINORS MUST BE WON!

COMPETITION CLOSES 31st JULY, 1963

WHAT YOU HAVE TO DO

Win a Mini-Minor

and a kiss

Competitions were beginning to be big news, and winning a car was the dream of many families.

Big Run On Electric Blankets

SALES of electric blankets are booming. In some Scottish shops, stocks running low.
Some makes are sold out.
One manufacturer has sold over 10 —their entire production for last ye Christmas. Now they're on overtime, still can't keep up with demand.
Another factory was cleaned out b

With more money available to many families, the purchase of modern home comforts was on the rise. Electric blankets were flying off the shelves.

The Sunday Post 2nd July 1961

The Sunday Post 5th December 1965

OOR WULLIE   FAMILY FUN!

IT MUST BE SMASHIN' BEING AN ANIMAL DOCTOR!

I'LL AWA' AND SEE IF THERE'S ANY ANIMALS NEEDIN' CURED O' ANYTHING!

JINGS! THERE'S A DOG WI' THE MEASLES!

THAT'S NO' MEASLES! THESE SPOTS ARE NATURAL! IT'S A DALMATIAN!

AW!

SAY 'AAH!', HORSEY!

HELP! IT'S NO' A DOCTOR YE NEED! IT'S A DENTIST! YER TEETH ARE LIKE AULD PIANO KEYS!

WHAT A SHAME! IT'S WING IS BROKEN!

HULLO! A JOB FOR ME AT LAST!

HUH! IT'S NO' A BIRD—IT'S AN AEROPLANE!

I SUPPOSE THESE DUCKS WILL HAVE THEIR OWN DOCTOR—A QUACK DOCTOR! HA-HA!

H'MM! THAT CAT DOESN'T LOOK TOO WELL!

HERE, CAT—LET'S FEEL YER PULSE!

HELP! IT'S GOIN' FOR ME!

SPIT!

HELP!

I GIVE UP! THESE ANIMALS DINNA WANT TO BE CURED!

CRIVVENS! YE'VE CAUGHT A CHILL, WULLIE! GET TO YER BED RIGHT AWAY!

SNIFF SNIFF

OKAY, MA!

SQUELCH!

POOR WEE LAD'S MISERABLE, PA! HE WIS PLAYIN' AT ANIMAL DOCTORS AN' GOT A DOOKIN'!

LEAVE IT TO ME, MA! I KNOW WHAT TO DO!

SOON

HERE'S MY HAMSTER, WULLIE!

AN' MY RABBIT!

AN' JEEMY MY MOOSE!

SQUEAK!

LOOK AT THAT! HE'S CHEERED UP ALREADY! THESE ANIMAL DOCTORS HAVE CURED HIM!

BETTER ALREADY!

The Sunday Post 7th July 1963

The Sunday Post 25th September 1966

OOR WULLIE FAMILY FUN!

The Sunday Post 11th June 1967

FESTIVE FUN AN' GAMES

Some of the most memorable of all Broons and Oor Wullie stories are those that appeared at Christmas or New Year. Even in the early days, when presents were in short supply, laughs were always plentiful.

Will the bairns get what they want from Santa and will the grown-ups have a ball at Hogmanay? You bet they will. And you're guaranteed a good time too, so sit back and enjoy this final selection of seldom-seen stories.

OOR WULLIE   FAMILY FUN!

The Sunday Post 24th December 1944

The Sunday Post 13th September 1936

1965-1969

By the second half of the sixties things were really 'swinging'. The Beatles ruled the pop world and at the cinema modern films such as Alfie and The Graduate competed with more traditional family friendly offerings of The Jungle Book and The Sound of Music. Travel moved forward at supersonic rate with the unveiling of Concorde while, at a more sedate pace, the QE 2 made her maiden voyage.

As the old 'steamies' were replaced by laundrettes, wash day became much easier – but just as sociable.

Sleek and simple the look of t... sixties.

A 'dream' sitting room from 1967. Note the ashtrays and serving hatch.

NOW – CHIPS FROM A SLOT MACHINE

THE latest slot machine serves you with a shilling's worth of chips on a plastic plate, with a plastic fork.

You can watch the chips being cooked through an observation window. They're ready in 45 seconds.

You get salt free by pressing another button. But it costs a 3d for sauce, vinegar or may

The firm is getting orders £820 machine from all o country. One is going to Sto A chain of Scottish pubs is of installing them.

> A good idea – but it didn't catch on.

> If diners wanted to avoid modern self service cafes, there were still plenty places where they could sit back and wait to be served.

TV COMMENT by Alan Stewart

WELL, after all the ballyhoo, what's the viewers' verdict on The Beatles fantasy "Magical Mystery Tour"? Sorry, lads, but it gets the thumbs-down!

● I've always been a Beatle fan, but I'm disillusioned after this.—Patricia Quinn (15), 24 Leith St., Riddrie.
● I waited anxiously to see this, but oh, what a disappointment.—D. Macleod, 217 Moraine Ave., Blairardie.
● How dare the B.B.C. show such an insult to our intelligence?—Mrs G. McMurrough, 89 Fellsview Ave., Kirkintilloch.
● In countless homes at sometime or other during a week viewing, someone must say, "That was a lot of trip said it after watching this. — Mrs Helen Wri Give me Cliff Richard and The Shadows any Cardenden Rd., Cardenden.

Keith, 54 Modley Pl., Ellon. Better luck next time, boys.

TITIPU — Sincere congratulations to Alan Melville and all concerned. The production could not be faulted.—Mrs M. McLachla

QUEEN'S SPEECH absolutely splendi striking reply to the who said the wh

> The Beatles may have been international stars, but not everything they did found favour with fans.

> The opening of the Tay Road Bridge gave fast access from Fife to Dundee.

He's The First Man In Britain To Rent Colour TV

MR HAROLD MONK, a retired pharmacist, of 14 Harborough Road, Sale, Cheshire, is the first person in Britain to rent a colour TV et.

He got the set a week ago. His rdict? Smashing!

Test card colour transmissions re made every day between 4 and .30.

Colour films are shown from 6.30 o 7.15.

One test card was a chrysanthe-um in full bloom. The colour was gnificent.

ne of the films was of the Alpine Rally, and it made it twice as citing to watch in Technicolor.

The set can receive B.B.C., ITV colour

to do is turn a knob, and the col bursts across the screen.

He can tune the colour until exactly right.

He has use faces judge

> The introduction of colour TV was a milestone in broadcasting history.

5000 FANS ARE FLYING TO WEMBLEY

NEARLY 5000 football fans are flying big Wembley game in April.

There's never been such a rush. B.E.A. are t solid, even with extra flights laid on. There's a British Eagle have bookings for 500. Some a match, they're leaving as early as Thursday. O British United Airways are laying on extr They've about 400 people waiting for seats.

The way things are going, everything that ampden Roar to London.

> Even football fans were moving with the times – literally.

Direct holiday flights from Glasgow to Spain & Italy

ing you more Just look at choose one ing direct

TOPSTAR Holidays by Air

PALMA (Majorca) 2 weeks holiday from (SPENDING MONEY £47)	£52.0s.
PUERTO SOLLER (Majorca) 2 weeks holiday from (SPENDING MONEY £44)	£58.0s.
SAN FELIU (Costa Brava) 15 days holiday from (SPENDING MONEY £50)	£48.10s.
LLORET DE MAR (Costa Brava) 15 days holiday from (SPENDING MONEY £51)	£49.18s.

> Direct flights made foreign holidays more accessible – while at home, the ever popular holiday camps offered fun for ALL the family.

HOTELS' NEW PLAN TO PREVENT BREATHALYSER TROUBLE

MOTORISTS who go for an evening out to a hotel function will soon be able to do so without worrying about the breathalyser test.

Instead of driving home, they'll be able to spend the night in the rate of £

The Trust hote No

ar

Ca Ge Hote Dunk of A Peebles.

The hotel been told

> With the introduction of breathalyser tests, some hotels planned to offer cheap rooms to encourage drinking!

DEAR SANTA CLAUS~ PLEASE, I WANT A DRUM, A BOX OF SOLDIERS, A TRAIN SET, A DOUBLE-DECKER BUS AN' A FORT!

XMAS EVE BUT, CRIVVENS! SANTA WILL NEVER GET A' THE TOYS I WANT IN MY WEE STOCKINGS!

AH! THERE'S THE RAGMAN PUSHIN' HIS BARROW UP THE BRAE~I'LL GIE HIM A HAND AN' HE'LL MAYBE GIE ME A BIG STOCKIN'!

I'LL GIE YE A SHOVE, MISTER.

THANKS, WULLIE, I'LL LOOK IN MA BAG WHEN WE GET UP THE BRAE. DAE YE HAE ONY BIG SOCKS?

YE SEE I NEED A BIG STOCKIN' FOR SANTA CLAUS TAE PIT MA TOYS IN.

I'LL SEE WHIT I'VE GOT.

THAT'S A' THERE IS.

AW! TWA BABY SOCKS! THAT'S NAE USE!

I'D GIE YE A PAIR O' MINE~BUT I DINNA WEAR ONY!

HEY, GEORDIE, YOUR PA'S A BIG MAN. COULD I BORROW ANE O' HIS BIG SOCKS TAE HANG UP FOR SANTA CLAUS?

COME IN TAE THE HOOSE AN' WE'LL LOOK FOR ANE.

HULLO, GEORDIE!

GEORDIE'S PA.

WE'D BETTER SNEAK IN BY THE WINDIE, FOR PA WID BE MAD IF HE KENT.

NA! THERE'S ONLY THESE THAT NEED WASHIN'. PA AYE WEARS THEM TILL THEY'RE STIFF.

HEY! WHIT'S GOIN' ON HERE?

WULLIE WANTED ANE O' YOUR SOCKS.

SOCKS? I'LL GIE HIM SOCKS!

DANNY, I BET A BIG LAD LIKE YOU HAS A BIG FAITHER WI' BIG FEET. COULD I GET THE LEN' O' ANE O' HIS BIG SOCKS? WHIT ARE YE LAUGHIN' AT?

HA! HA!

HA! HA! LOOK! THAT'S MA FAITHER GOIN' DOON THE ROAD WI' MA MITHER AN' OOR DOG!

LATER THERE'S SOMETHING WRONG WITH THIS AERIAL. OUR WIRELESS WON'T WORK.

HURRY UP AND GET IT FIXED.

THOUGHT~ JINGS! THE SUPERINTENDENT'S BLAZIN'!

WULLIE'S HOOSE

NAE WONDER IT WINNA WORK WI' JUIST A WEE BIT WIRE LIKE THAT!

MA LUCK'S IN AT LAST! I'LL FIX THEM UP WI' SOME AULD WIRELESS WIRE OOT O' MA SHED~ THEN I'LL MAYBE GET A BIG PAIR O' SOCKS FRAE THEM, FOR THEY'RE A' BIG LADS.

Wullie's Shed

HERE IT IS! I'LL FIX IT TAE OOR GREENIE POLES~THEN~

~TIE THE OTHER END TAE THEIR ARIEL.

I CANNA FIND MA CLAES ROPE ONY PLACE. BUT I'LL HANG MA WASHIN' ON THIS WIRE. I WONDER WHIT WULLIE PUT IT UP FOR?

AH, GOOD! THE RADIO'S GOING WELL NOW!

I FIXED IT UP FOR YE! DAE YE HAE ONY SOCKS?

DINNA TELL LIES. AN' DINNA ASK CHEEKY QUESTIONS. AWA' YE GO, NOW!

HEY! COME BACK WI' MA WASHIN'! WHA'S TIED IT TAE THE BACK O' THAT POLICE CAR? IT'S WULLIE~STOP! STOP!

STOP THE CAR! WE'RE BEING FOLLOWED!

JINGS! IT'S TIME I WISNA HERE!

THAT NIGHT HUH! HOW DID I NO' THINK O' THIS AFORE? I DINNA NEED A STOCKIN' AT A'. I'VE HUNG UP MA BUCKET!

S. CLAUS~ KPIT IT IN MA BUCKET

XMAS MORNING WHOOPEE! SANTA'S BEEN~WI' A' THE TOYS I WANTED!

TRAIN SET

DUDLEY D. WATKINS

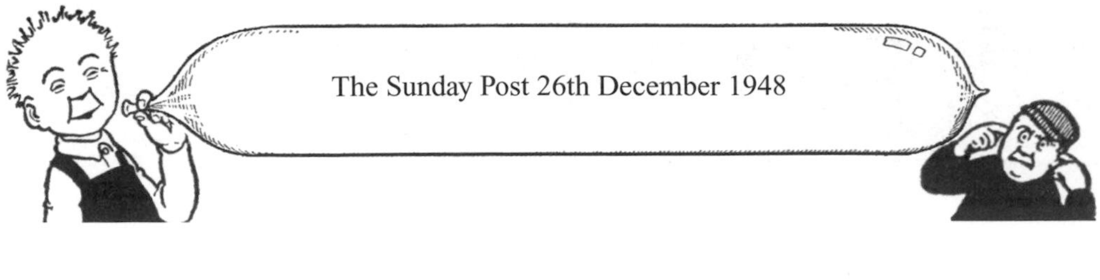

The Sunday Post 26th December 1948

PAW BROON

MAW BROON   HEN BROON

MAGGIE BROON   JOE BROON

DAPHNE BROON

HORACE BROON

THE BROON TWINS

THE BROON BAIRN

GRAN'PAW BROON

The Sunday Post 26th December 1937

OOR WULLIE FAMILY FUN!

The Sunday Post 22nd December 1968

PAW BROON   MAW BROON   HEN BROON   MAGGIE BROON   JOE BROON   DAPHNE BROON   HORACE BROON   THE BROON TWINS   THE BROON BAIRN   GRAN'PAW BROON

The Sunday Post 21st December 1952

The Sunday Post 31st December 1950

The Sunday Post 28th December 1958